TULLUS

AND THE DARK CITY

Chariot Books™

David C. Cook Publishing Co.

SAnDers

Published by Chariot Books,
an imprint of David C. Cook Publishing Co.
David C. Cook Publishing Co., Elgin, Illinois 60120
David C. Cook Publishing Co., Weston, Ontario
Nova Distribution, Ltd., Newton Abbot, England

TULLUS AND THE DARK CITY
©1993 by David C. Cook Publishing Co.

Cover illustration by David Darrow
Cover design by Stephen D. Smith
Interior design by Paul Mouw

First printing, 1993
Printed in the United States of America
97 96 95 94 93 5 4 3 2 1

Library of Congress Cataloging-in-Publication Data
CIP applied for

TULLUS AND THE CAVES OF GOREME

TULLUS
AND THE DARK CITY

FOREWORD

THIS ADVENTURE TAKES PLACE IN THE GOREME VALLEY, TURKEY, NOW A GREAT TOURIST ATTRACTION.

•

AGES AGO A SERIES OF VOLCANIC EXPLOSIONS SHOWERED A VAST AREA WITH TUFFSTONE--A SOFT VOLCANIC ASH--MANY HUNDREDS OF FEET IN DEPTH.

THROUGHOUT TIME, WIND AND RAIN HAVE CUT THIS ASH INTO A NIGHTMARE OF FANTASTIC CONE-SHAPED OUTCROPPINGS.

•

FOR CENTURIES, NATIVES HAVE DUG CAVE HOMES IN THESE CONES OF TUFFSTONE. EARLY CHRISTIANS FOUND REFUGE FROM PERSECUTION HERE AND DUG UNDERGROUND CHURCHES WITH WALLS BEAUTIFULLY DECORATED WITH FRESCOES OF BIBLICAL SCENES.

6

7

AFTER TULLUS CHECKS THE HORSES...

THEY ARE WELL STABLED. I'LL PRAY FOR YOUR CALM AND SAFE JOURNEY.

AND I FOR YOURS. BY THE WAY, YOU HAVE YOUR TRAVEL PERMIT, I TRUST.

SINCE WHEN HAVE ROMAN CITIZENS NEEDED TRAVEL PERMITS?

ONLY HERE, BECAUSE IT'S TOO EASY FOR SLAVES AND DESERTERS TO ESCAPE INTO ARMENIA WHERE THEY FIND REFUGE.

TULLUS GOES FOR A TRAVEL PERMIT...

CAESAREA-MAZACA*? THAT'S A DANGEROUS PART OF THE EMPIRE. YOU'LL HAVE TO SIGN A RELEASE FREEING THE GOVERNOR FROM ALL RESPONSIBILITY FOR YOUR SAFETY.

*TODAY, KAYSERI, TURKEY

HAVE THIS PASS SIGNED WHEN YOU ARRIVE THERE AND TURN IT IN HERE WHEN YOU GET BACK. IF YOU DON'T RETURN WITHIN SIX MONTHS YOU MIGHT LOSE YOUR CITIZENSHIP. THAT'S ALL. NEXT...

HE'S THE ONE I HEARD TALKING ABOUT CHRISTIANS IN CAPPADOCIA. SHOULD I TURN HIM IN?

DON'T GET ME INVOLVED. TELL YOUR CENTURION.

8

THE SOLDIER TELLS HIS OFFICER...

I CAN'T ARREST HIM ON JUST YOUR WORD. HE'S A ROMAN CITIZEN. BUT HE MIGHT LEAD US TO A GROUP OF CHRISTIANS IF HE'S FOLLOWED...

LATER, IN THE SOLDIERS' BARRACKS...

WHY THE PEASANT COSTUME? YOU GOING TO DESERT?

DESERT? NOT ME! THE CENTURION'S SENDING ME ON A MISSION. I MAY GET A PROMOTION!

AT DAWN NEXT MORNING, TULLUS AND HIS HORSE, BLAZE, JOIN A CARAVAN.

GLAD YOU GOT HERE ON TIME. WE'RE READY TO START. I HAVE A MAN WHO WILL BE YOUR GROOM.

GOOD. I'LL GO OVER AND MEET HIM. START YOUR CARAVAN. I'M ALL SET TO GO.

SO FAR THE WEATHER HAS BEEN FAIR. BUT NOW AFTER THE CARAVAN STOPS FOR THE NIGHT, A COLD WIND SWEEPS IN FROM THE NORTH BRINGING SNOW-LADEN CLOUDS WITH ITS ICY BLAST. SOON THE SNOW BEGINS TO FALL, BLANKETING BEASTS AND TENTS...

THE WIND INCREASES TO A FIERCE BLIZZARD. THE CARAVAN LEADER RUSHES OUT OF HIS TENT...

UP! UP! WE MUST MOVE OUT! HURRY!

TENTS ARE QUICKLY STRUCK BY THE EXPERIENCED COMPANY DESPITE THE HOWLING GALE...THE CAMELEERS LOAD THEIR GRUMBLING BEASTS, AND WITHIN A SHORT WHILE THE CARAVAN IS ON ITS WAY TO SEEK A MORE SHELTERED PLACE TO WAIT OUT THE STORM.

THE WINDBLOWN SNOW IS NOW FORMING DEEP DRIFTS. VELI'S HORSE STUMBLES, THROWING ITS RIDER...

FORTUNATELY, TULLUS HEARS HIS YELLS ABOVE THE HOWLING GALE...

VELI REFUSES TO RIDE HIS HORSE.

THE STORM IS LESSENING. WE SHOULD CATCH UP TO THE OTHERS SOON.

A FEW HOURS LATER...

MASTER--I CAN'T GO ANY FURTHER.

THERE'S A SHELTERED PLACE. WE'LL REST AWHILE. THE OTHERS CAN'T BE FAR. THEY MUST REST TOO.

AFTER A SHORT REST...

NOT A FOOTSTEP BREAKS THE SNOWY CRUST! HOW CAN A WHOLE CARAVAN DISAPPEAR LIKE THAT?

EVIL SPIRITS, THAT'S WHAT IT IS!

TULLUS CONVINCES VELI THAT IF THEY ARE TO CATCH UP TO THE CARAVAN, HE HAD BETTER RIDE. UNTIL LATE AT NIGHT THEY FOLLOW WHAT THEY HOPE IS THE DIRECTION THE CARAVAN TOOK.

THIS CHRISTIAN IS BEWITCHED. THE PRIESTS OF MITHRAS WARNED US ABOUT THEM.

NEXT DAWN...

VELI IS GONE! HE'S TAKEN BOTH HORSES WITH ALL THE FOOD AND GEAR!

TULLUS CLIMBS A HIGH PINNACLE TO SEARCH THE HORIZON--AND QUICKLY CLAMBERS DOWN WHEN BOTH HORSES COME TROTTING BACK.

SURE THAT VELI HAS AGAIN FALLEN OFF HIS HORSE, TULLUS RETRACES THEIR TRAIL AND COMES TO VELI LYING UNCONSCIOUS WHERE HIS HEAD HAD HIT A ROCK!

TULLUS GETS VELI ONTO HIS HORSE AND SECURES HIM WITH THE BLANKET STRAP. SOON HE COMES TO A TRAIL LEADING DOWN FROM THE PLATEAU AND FOLLOWS IT TO A GRASSY PLAIN BELOW.

COMING TO A SMALL STREAM, TULLUS STOPS TO REST THE HORSES AND EAT THE LAST OF THE FOOD HE HAS CARRIED. VELI RECOVERS WHEN TULLUS BATHES HIS WOUND, BUT REFUSES TO SPEAK OR EAT THE FOOD TULLUS OFFERS HIM. HE SITS OFF BY HIMSELF STARING INTO THE DISTANCE.

AFTER A SHORT REST, TULLUS PACKS, MOUNTS BLAZE, AND HOLDS THE OTHER HORSE. VELI HESITATES, THEN SILENTLY MOUNTS AND FOLLOWS TULLUS. LATER IN THE AFTERNOON, THEY COME TO A SHEPHERD TENDING HIS FLOCK.

HO, STRANGERS! YOU HAVE WANDERED FAR FROM THE USUAL CARAVAN ROUTES. WHAT SEEK THEE IN THE VALLEY OF GOREME?

THE VALLEY OF GOREME? AH! GOD ANSWERED MY PRAYERS AND DIRECTED ME TO MY GOAL! WE LOST OUR CARAVAN IN A BLIZZARD.

YOUR GOAL?

I HEARD OF A CHRISTIAN COLONY HERE AND LEFT BYZANTIUM TO VISIT IT. I AM A CHRISTIAN FROM ROME.

TULLUS INTRODUCES VELI BUT DOES NOT MENTION HIS ATTEMPTED DESERTION. THE KINDLY SHEPHERD INVITES THEM TO STAY THE NIGHT IN HIS HUMBLE SOD COTTAGE WHERE HE LIVES WITH HIS DAUGHTER DURING HIS TURN AT GRAZING THE COLONY'S SHEEP. IT IS THE COLONY'S CUSTOM TO SHARE ALL LABOR AND ALL MATERIAL THINGS.

THEY ALL LISTEN INTENTLY AS TULLUS TELLS THEM OF THE ROMAN CHRISTIANS WHO KEEP THEIR FAITH DESPITE PERSECUTION AND OF OTHERS WHOM HE HAS MET IN HIS TRAVELS.

NEXT DAY, LISA, THE DAUGHTER, GUIDES TULLUS AND VELI TO THE COLONY. HER FATHER STAYS WITH HIS FLOCK AND THE TWO HORSES.

YOU MEAN TO SAY PEOPLE ACTUALLY LIVE IN CAVES DUG INTO THOSE CONES?

YES, AND UNDERGROUND AS WELL!

16

WHY DON'T YOU TAKE OUR VISITORS TO OUR CHURCH, FATHER? LISA AND I WILL WAIT HERE.

I'LL BE HAPPY TO. COME, FRIENDS, FOLLOW ME.

TAKING TORCHES FROM A STACK INSIDE THE DOOR AND LIGHTING THEM FROM A BRAZIER OF BURNING COALS, THEY DESCEND TO A VAST UNDERGROUND MAZE OF TUNNELS AND VAULTS HAND-CARVED OUT OF SOLID TUFFSTONE.

WHEN THEY REACH THE CHAPEL...

THIS IS AMAZING! THE CATACOMBS OF ROME ARE NOTHING LIKE THIS! AND THE BEAUTIFUL PAINTINGS ON THE WALLS AND COLUMNS! THIS IS TRULY GOD-INSPIRED!

SUDDENLY FROM ONE OF THE AIR SHAFTS...

A TROOP OF ROMAN CAVALRY HEADING THIS WAY! TAKE COVER!

HA! EVERYONE WILL HIDE UNDERGROUND! THE VILLAGE WILL BE EMPTY!

NOW'S MY CHANCE! I'LL GO BACK TO THE SURFACE AND GUIDE THE TROOPS DOWN HERE!

WHILE TULLUS AND HIS GUIDE MOVE ON, VELI LAGS BEHIND, THEN SNEAKS OFF TOWARD AN EXIT.

BUT THE CORRIDOR LEADS DOWN NOT UP! ON AND ON HE WANDERS ALONG, LOSING ALL SENSE OF DIRECTION AND TIME. HIS FEAR GROWS INTO PANIC. HE STARTS TO RUN, STUMBLES, AND DROPS HIS TORCH LEAVING HIM IN TOTAL BLACKNESS.

MEANWHILE, THE VILLAGERS HAVE FLED INTO THEIR UNDERGROUND REFUGE. LISA AND ANDROS RUN INTO TULLUS AND HIS GUIDE, ANDROS'S FATHER.

YOU SAY THE OTHER ROMAN DISAPPEARED RIGHT AFTER THE SOLDIERS WERE REPORTED? DO YOU TRUST HIM, TULLUS?

I THINK THE POOR FELLOW IS SO FULL OF FEAR SINCE WE WERE LOST, HE CAN'T STOP RUNNING!

THE ROMANS HAVE OFTEN TRIED TO PLANT SPIES AMONG US. WE CAN'T TAKE A CHANCE THIS MAN ISN'T ONE. HE MUST BE FOUND.

I FEEL RESPONSIBLE FOR HIM. HOW CAN I HELP?

WHILE SOME OF US GO TO CONFUSE THE ROMANS IF THEY FIND ONE OF OUR ENTRANCES, YOU GO WITH THE FERRET TO HUNT FOR YOUR MAN. THE FERRET KNOWS THESE CAVERNS LIKE THE PALM OF HIS HAND.

A ROMAN? HE SHOULD NOT BE HARD TO TRACK. OUR PEOPLE HAVE ALL TAKEN ONE PATH.

SEE? IT IS A FLAT-SOLED SANDAL, WITH A HOLE IN THE HEEL. IT LEADS AWAY FROM THE USUAL PATH. HE CAN EASILY GET LOST THIS WAY.

AFTER HOURS OF FEELING HIS WAY IN TOTAL BLACKNESS, VELI BUMPS INTO A LONG FLIGHT OF STEPS...

LIGHT! LIGHT! HO! LAND OF DARKNESS, I'VE BEATEN YOU! I'M FREE, I'M FREE!

VELI HAS ACCIDENTALLY STUMBLED ON A SECRET DOOR TO THE UNDERGROUND SANCTUARY JUST AS THE ROMAN TROOP WAS ABOUT TO QUIT THE VILLAGE.

HO! THERE'S THE ONLY LIVING THING WE'VE SEEN IN THE ACCURSED PLACE! CAPTURE HIM! WE'LL MAKE HIM TELL US WHERE THE PEOPLE ARE HIDING!

BUT THE SUDDEN RELEASE FROM THE FEAR AND BLACKNESS PROVE TOO MUCH FOR VELI.

TOO LATE! YOU'LL GET NO INFORMATION FROM THIS ONE, SIR. HE NO LONGER LIVES.

DEMONS, BAH! THE ROMAN EAGLE FEARS NO MAN OR DEMON!

THE DEMONS IN THERE HAVE TAKEN HIS SPIRIT!

TAKING TORCHES FROM NEARBY CAVES THE ROMANS INVADE THE UNDERGROUND CORRIDORS IN SEARCH OF CAPTIVES...

THE FERRET HAS FOLLOWED VELI'S TRACKS WITHOUT LOSING ANY TIME. SOON AFTER HE HAS FOUND VELI'S LOST TORCH, HE STOPS BY A GRILLE IN THE WALL...

HA! LISTEN! THE ROMANS HAVE ENTERED YOUR CAVERN. SOUNDS LIKE AT SECTOR 22!

YOU MEAN YOU CAN ACTUALLY HEAR ANYONE ENTERING HERE AND JUDGE WHERE?

THESE CAVERNS ARE HONEYCOMBED WITH LISTENING AND TALKING DUCTS. THERE ARE ALSO GRILLES ON THE FLOORS AND CEILINGS OF THE CORRIDORS THROUGH WHICH SPEARS AND ARROWS CAN BE THRUST. WE HAVE BEEN FORCED TO DESTROY MANY INVADERS. BUT USUALLY WE ARE ABLE TO MERELY FRIGHTEN THEM OFF!

I AM HOPING WE CAN MAKE THESE ROMANS GO BACK WITHOUT BLOODSHED.

SPOKEN AS A TRUE CHRISTIAN! IT IS OUR HOPE ALSO. WE'LL GET TO WORK ON THEIR PAGAN SUPERSTITIONS.

BEWARE, ROMANS! YOU HAVE ENTERED THE CAVES OF GOREME AGAINST THE WILL OF THOSE WHO DWELL HERE!

RETURN TO THE OUTSIDE WORLD WHILE YOU MAY. IF YOU ADVANCE FURTHER YOU WILL SURELY BE LOST!

YOU WILL NEVER SEE THE UPPER WORLD AGAIN IF YOU REMAIN UNTIL YOUR TORCHES BURN OUT.

IF YOU CAN GUIDE ME TO THE ROMANS I'D LIKE TO FACE THEM. IT WOULD BE BETTER IF THEY LEFT BECAUSE OF REASON RATHER THAN FEAR.

YOU MAY BE RIGHT. BUT YOU ALSO MAY BE KILLED. THEY ARE VERY NERVOUS NOW!

WHILE THE FERRET LEADS TULLUS BY SIDE CORRIDORS TO THE ROMANS, PANIC BEGINS TO MOUNT AS ONE BY ONE THEIR TORCHES SPUTTER OUT...

WE'LL BE TRAPPED IN THE DARK.

LET'S GET BACK TO THE SURFACE.

STOP!

THE 30TH LEGION HAS NEVER RETREATED FROM MAN OR DEMON. WE'RE NOT GOING TO BEFOUL THAT RECORD!

AT THAT CRITICAL MOMENT, TULLUS STEPS OUT OF A SIDE CORRIDOR.

HAIL, FELLOW ROMANS! I GREET YOU WHO HAVE PROVED THE COURAGE OF LEGIONNAIRES BY ENTERING THE DARK UNDERGROUND CITY OF GOREME!

IS HE SPIRIT OR FLESH?

HIS ACCENT IS TRUE ROMAN!

YOUR MISSION IS ACCOMPLISHED WITH HONOR. THERE ARE NONE HERE BUT PEACEFUL CITIZENS, WOMEN, AND CHILDREN. THE FIGHTING MEN OF THE 30TH LEGION DO NOT MAKE WAR ON THEM. COME, FOLLOW US!

THE FERRET GUIDES THE GROUP TO A DIFFERENT EXIT THAN THE DOOR THE SOLDIERS HAD ENTERED BY.

OPEN SKY ABOVE ONCE AGAIN!

AND AIR! FRESH AIR!

AND THE MOON! THE STARS!

BY MEANS OF THEIR AMAZING COMMUNICATING SYSTEM, THE CHRISTIANS ON LISTENING DUTY HAVE HEARD EVERYTHING. THE FERRET, WHO HAS NOT COME OUTSIDE AFTER SHOWING TULLUS THE WAY, TELLS THE LISTENERS TO HAVE THE ROMANS' HORSES DRIVEN TO WHERE THE ROMANS CAME UP FROM UNDERGROUND.

OUR HORSES! HOW'D THEY KNOW WHERE WE ARE?

WE DIDN'T PICKET THEM HERE!

NO ONE IS DRIVING THEM TO US!

DON'T STAND THERE GAPING! GRAB THE HORSES!

THE CENTURION TURNS TO TULLUS...

THANK YOU FOR GETTING US OUT OF A NASTY SITUATION. I HAVE NO HEART FOR CAPTURING INNOCENT CHRISTIANS. I AM A SOLDIER! NOW, I CAN TRUTHFULLY REPORT THAT THE ONLY PERSON ALIVE IN GOREME WAS A TRAVELING ROMAN CITIZEN.

AS SOON AS THE ROMAN TROOP HAS DISAPPEARED, THE VILLAGERS EMERGE FROM THE UNDERGROUND CHURCH SINGING.

THEY FIND THE BODY OF VELI WHERE THE ROMANS LEFT IT AND GIVE HIM A DECENT BURIAL. TULLUS DECIDES TO STAY FOR A WHILE WITH THE KINDLY CHRISTIANS LIVING IN THE STRANGE CAVES OF GOREME.

Tullus

and the Kidnapped Prince

Part II

BOTH LIE ASLEEP, HIDDEN FROM THE ROAD BY HIGH GRASS AS THE TWO WOULD-BE ABDUCTORS RIDE PAST, SEARCHING FOR THE BOY.

I DO NOT LIKE THIS. HOW COULD THAT LITTLE IMP DISAPPEAR SO COMPLETELY UNLESS A GENIE CARRIED HIM OFF?

BAH! I CANNOT BELIEVE THAT!

EVEN RAVANA, THE DEMON KING WITH HIS TWENTY ARMS*, COULD NOT CARRY OFF THAT SLIPPERY YOUNG ONE!

*ONE OF THE MANY HINDU GODS

BY PURE CHANCE, THE TWO COME TO THE SAME LITTLE VILLAGE TOWARD WHICH TULLUS AND PRINCE BHARAT ARE HEADING, AND WHERE THE BOY'S NURSE IS WAITING.

WE'LL WATER OUR HORSES HERE AND GET FOOD BEFORE WE CONTINUE THE SEARCH.

AND WE HAD BETTER FIND THAT BOY OR THE KING WILL HAVE OUR HEADS!

WAKE UP IN THERE, WAKE UP! OPEN THE DOOR BEFORE I KICK IT IN!

THEY FRIGHTEN THE POOR FAMILY INTO GIVING THEM FOOD. IN ANOTHER ROOM OF THE COTTAGE THE NURSE OVERHEARS THEM TALKING AND REALIZES THEY ARE THE KIDNAPPERS AND THAT SOMEHOW THE PRINCE HAS ESCAPED FROM THEM, PROBABLY WITH TULLUS'S HELP.

PRINCE BHARAT AND THAT STRANGER MAY BE COMING HERE! I MUST TRY TO WARN THEM! BUT HOW AND WHERE?

27

28

WAIT? WHAT DO YOU WANT HIM TO WAIT FOR?

DON'T YOU SEE WHAT I SEE?

THE BOY IS JUST ABOUT THE SAME AGE AS THE PRINCE!

OUR KING HAS NEVER SEEN THE PRINCE. WE'LL TAKE THIS BOY TO HIM, COLLECT OUR REWARD, AND DISAPPEAR!

HA! YOU ARE RIGHT! HE'LL NEVER KNOW THE DIFFERENCE.

GO TELL YOUR FATHER TO COME HERE AT ONCE, BOY!

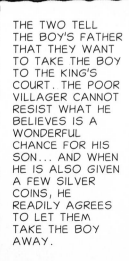

THE TWO TELL THE BOY'S FATHER THAT THEY WANT TO TAKE THE BOY TO THE KING'S COURT. THE POOR VILLAGER CANNOT RESIST WHAT HE BELIEVES IS A WONDERFUL CHANCE FOR HIS SON... AND WHEN HE IS ALSO GIVEN A FEW SILVER COINS, HE READILY AGREES TO LET THEM TAKE THE BOY AWAY.

THAT WAS EASIER THAN I THOUGHT IT WOULD BE!

IT IS A BRILLIANT PLAN. IT CAN'T GO WRONG!

29

THIS SCHEME CAN'T FAIL! THE KING WILL BELIEVE THIS BOY IS THE PRINCE, AND WE'LL BE SAFE!

WHAT IF THE REAL PRINCE BHARAT SHOWS UP?

SHOWS UP IN THE KINGDOM OF HIS FATHER'S DEADLY ENEMY? NEVER!

YOU'RE RIGHT. BESIDES, AS SOON AS WE COLLECT OUR REWARD, WE'LL LEAVE THE KINGDOM FOR GOOD!

IN THE MEANTIME, TULLUS AND THE REAL PRINCE BHARAT WAKE UP FROM THEIR SLEEP IN THE FIELD OF HIGH GRASS.

WAKE UP, PRINCE! IT'S TIME TO GO.

THEY HAVEN'T GONE FAR WHEN THEY ARE MET BY THE PRINCE'S NURSE...

STOP! STOP! YOU MUSTN'T GO TO THE VILLAGE! THOSE TWO MEN ARE THERE!

THE NURSE TELLS THEM OF THE CONVERSATION SHE OVERHEARD...

THEY SAID THEY'D DO TERRIBLE THINGS TO YOU WHEN THEY CAUGHT YOU!

I'LL DO WORSE TO THEM WHEN I CATCH UP WITH THEM!

NOW, PRINCE...

STOP BABYING ME, BOTH OF YOU. YOU FORGET I AM PRINCE BHARAT!

NO ONE CAN LAY HANDS ON ME WITHOUT BEING PUNISHED! I'M NOT AFRAID OF THOSE TWO. LET'S GO GET THEM!

ER--LET'S GO TO YOUR HOME FIRST!

TULLUS AND THE NURSE PERSUADE THE HOTHEADED YOUNG PRINCE THAT IT WOULD BE BEST TO FOREGO HIS THOUGHTS OF REVENGE FOR THE PRESENT AND RETURN TO HIS HOME.

WHILE HE AND TULLUS REMAIN HIDDEN, THE NURSE ARRANGES FOR A NEW WHEEL TO BE PUT ON THE CART AND HIRES A VILLAGER WITH A TEAM OF OXEN TO DRAW IT.

THEN THEY START OFF FOR THE PRINCE'S HOME.

YOU ARE IN VERY GOOD SPIRITS TODAY, FRIEND.

YES, SAHIB! THIS HAS BEEN A MOST LUCKY DAY FOR ME.

ON THE WAY TO PRINCE BHARAT'S HOME, TULLUS STRIKES UP A CONVERSATION WITH THE DRIVER...

YOU PEOPLE HIRE ME TO DRAW YOUR CART WITH MY OXEN AND EARLIER TWO STRANGERS TOOK A LIKING TO MY SON AND PAID ME TO LET THEM TAKE HIM TO LIVE AT THE KING'S PALACE!

HEARING THIS, BOTH PRINCE BHARAT AND HIS NURSE STICK THEIR HEADS OUT FROM THE CART...

WHAT'S THIS ABOUT TWO STRANGERS AND YOUR SON?

WHAT DID THEY LOOK LIKE?

32

THE DRIVER TELLS THEM THE WHOLE STORY AND DESCRIBES THE TWO MEN...

THOSE ARE THE SAME MEN WHO WERE THREATENING PRINCE BHARAT!

THE TWO WHO TRIED TO KIDNAP ME!

DID I DO WRONG, SAHIB? IS MY BOY IN DANGER? HE IS BUT A CHILD LIKE THE YOUNG SAHIB HERE!

SUDDENLY THE TERRIBLE TRUTH DAWNS ON TULLUS!

THEY'RE GOING TO PASS OFF THAT BOY AS PRINCE BHARAT! THEY'LL SLAY HIM! HOW CAN MEN BE SO EVIL?

WHAT ARE YOU THINKING?

QUICK! TELL ME THE ROAD THEY WOULD MOST LIKELY TAKE TO THAT KINGDOM!

THEY WOULD TAKE THIS ONE, SAHIB, THEN TURN INTO THE HILLS AT THE FIRST FORK.

NOW WHERE IS HE OFF TO?

WAIT! WAIT! TAKE ME WITH YOU!

I MUST CONVINCE THE KING THAT THE BOY IS NOT PRINCE BHARAT! HELP ME, O GOD, HELP ME!

THEY CAN'T BE TOO FAR AHEAD OF ME. HELP ME, O LORD, TO OVERTAKE THEM!

IF THEY TAKE A DIFFERENT ROAD PERHAPS I CAN REACH THE KING BEFORE THEY DO AND CONVINCE HIM THE BOY IS NOT PRINCE BHARAT!

THE REAL PRINCE BHARAT IS IN A RAGE BECAUSE TULLUS LEFT HIM BEHIND.

CAN'T YOU MAKE THESE DUMB BEASTS MOVE FASTER? I'VE GOT TO CATCH UP WITH THAT MAN!

THEY HAVE BUT TWO SPEEDS, SAHIB...SLOW AND STOP.

MEANWHILE, THE MEN WITH THE BOY PLAN THEIR NEXT MOVES.

HOW WILL WE PASS HIM OFF AS THE PRINCE IN THESE RAGS?

WE'LL GET HIM NEW CLOTHES BEFORE WE SHOW HIM TO THE KING.

YOU ARE GOING TO GIVE ME NEW CLOTHES AND TAKE ME TO A KING?

AYE, KUBERA* SMILES UPON YOU.

*HINDU GOD OF WEALTH.

BUT YOU MUST DO EXACTLY AS WE TELL YOU OR YOU WILL BE TAKEN AWAY BY DEMONS!

OH, SIRS, I WILL DO EVERYTHING YOU TELL ME. NEW CLOTHES AND MEETING A KING! I AM INDEED LUCKY!

FIRST, YOU MUST LEARN YOUR NEW NAME. FROM NOW ON YOU ARE PRINCE BHARAT. CAN YOU REMEMBER THAT?

PRINCE BHARAT! PRINCE BHARAT. DOES THAT MEAN I AM TO BE A REAL PRINCE?

FOR THE REST OF YOUR LIFE...

WHICH WON'T BE LONG ONCE THE KING GETS YOU!

ALL THAT DAY, AS THEY RIDE UP AND UP ALONG THE TWISTING TRAIL THAT LEADS OVER THE HIGH PASS THROUGH THE MOUNTAINS, THE TWO MEN INSTRUCT THE LAD IN HIS ROLE AS PRINCE BHARAT.

THE INNOCENT BOY ENTERS INTO THE SCHEME WHOLEHEARTEDLY... HE BELIEVES THE TWO MEN ARE ACTUALLY GOING TO MAKE HIM A PRINCE!

TOWARD EVENING THEY OVERTAKE A CARAVAN OF PLODDING CAMELS.

HO! YOU THERE! PULL YOUR CAMELS TO ONE SIDE AND LET US PASS!

GLADLY, STRANGER, GLADLY, IF THEY COULD CLING TO THE CLIFF AS DO FLIES.

WE MUST GET PAST. WE CAN'T SPEND THE NIGHT HERE!

WE DON'T INTEND TO EITHER, STRANGER. BUT YOU CAN SEE THERE'S NO ROOM TO GET BY.

BE PATIENT FOR A FEW MILES AND YOU'LL BE WELCOME TO SHARE OUR FIRE THROUGH THE NIGHT.

THEY HAVE NO CHOICE BUT TO FOLLOW THE PLODDING CARAVAN ALONG THE PATH.

FINALLY, THEY COME TO A WIDE PLAIN WHERE THE CARAVAN HALTS FOR THE NIGHT.

AT LAST. NOW WE CAN GET AHEAD OF THEM.

NO! LET'S CAMP WITH THEM FOR THE NIGHT. WE CAN LEAVE BEFORE THEM AT DAWN.

COME OVER HERE, STRANGERS. JOIN OUR FIRE AND SHARE OUR FOOD.

MIGHTY TIRED, AREN'T YOU, BLAZE. AS SOON AS WE COME TO A LIKELY SPOT WE'LL STOP.

SOON...

GOD IS WATCHING OVER US, BLAZE. HERE IS GRASS FOR YOU AND THERE IS A TRICKLE OF WATER TO EASE OUR THIRST.

WHILE BLAZE CROPS THE SWEET GRASS, TULLUS PRAYS, THANKING GOD FOR HIS PROTECTION AND ASKING FOR HIS HELP IN SAVING THE YOUNG VILLAGE BOY FROM HARM.

AND FAR BEHIND, PRINCE BHARAT ALSO AGREES FINALLY TO CALL A HALT FOR THE NIGHT.

WE MUST STOP, PRINCE! WE ARE ALL TOO WEARY TO CONTINUE.

AYE, SAHIB. THE BEASTS MUST BE UNYOKED AND ALLOWED TO REST!

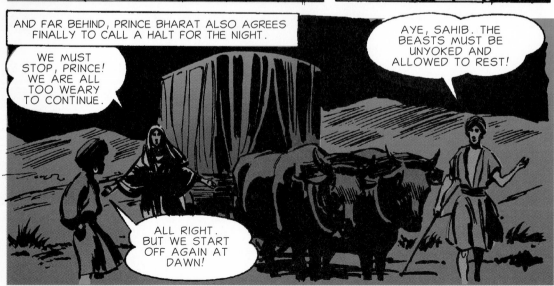

ALL RIGHT. BUT WE START OFF AGAIN AT DAWN!

AFTER PRAYING, TULLUS EATS THE FEW BARLEY CAKES HE HAS WITH HIM. THEN, BEFORE HE LIES DOWN TO SLEEP HE GIVES BLAZE A RUBDOWN WITH SOME DRY GRASS.

WHILE AT THE CARAVAN CAMP, THE DRIVERS DISCUSS THE TWO STRANGERS AND THE BOY.

GOD WILL ANSWER MY PRAYERS, BLAZE, I KNOW. OUR LORD JESUS PROMISED THAT WHATSOEVER WE ASK IN HIS NAME SHALL COME TO PASS!

A PRINCE WOULD HAVE A HORSE OF HIS OWN.

OR MAKE HIS SERVANT WALK!

THIS BOY IS ABOUT THE PRINCE'S AGE. I SAW HIM LAST YEAR...

"THE PRINCE'S FATHER IS A GREAT HORSEMAN. I WATCHED HIM PLAY A GAME CALLED POLO. THE YOUNG PRINCE WAS THERE. I SAW HIM CLEARLY."

NOTE: POLO IS THOUGHT TO HAVE ORIGINATED IN PERSIA ABOUT 4,000 YEARS AGO. THE WORD "POLO" IS FROM A TIBETAN DIALECT MEANING THE BALL USED IN THE GAME. IT HAS ALWAYS BEEN A POPULAR GAME IN INDIA.

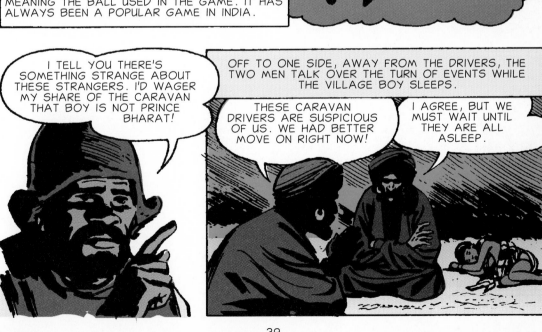

I TELL YOU THERE'S SOMETHING STRANGE ABOUT THESE STRANGERS. I'D WAGER MY SHARE OF THE CARAVAN THAT BOY IS NOT PRINCE BHARAT!

OFF TO ONE SIDE, AWAY FROM THE DRIVERS, THE TWO MEN TALK OVER THE TURN OF EVENTS WHILE THE VILLAGE BOY SLEEPS.

THESE CARAVAN DRIVERS ARE SUSPICIOUS OF US. WE HAD BETTER MOVE ON RIGHT NOW!

I AGREE, BUT WE MUST WAIT UNTIL THEY ARE ALL ASLEEP.

AND THE CARAVAN DRIVERS, TOO, WHISPER TOGETHER BY THEIR SMALL COOKING FIRE...

WHY DID THEY LEAVE OUR FIRE? THEY ATE OUR FOOD BUT WILL NOT TALK WITH US.

THEY ARE HIDING SOMETHING, AND I WARRANT IT IS NOT GOOD!

PERHAPS IF WE COULD DISCOVER THEIR SECRET, WE COULD PROFIT! BUT COME, LET US GET SOME SLEEP.

FARTHER BACK ON THE ROAD, TULLUS AND BLAZE SETTLE DOWN FOR A FEW HOURS SLEEP.

AND STILL FARTHER BACK, PRINCE BHARAT AND HIS COMPANIONS ALSO SLEEP.

40

NEXT MORNING...

HAVING NO CHOICE, AND FEARING FOR THEIR VERY LIVES, THE TWO MEN TELL HOW THEY WERE HIRED TO KIDNAP PRINCE BHARAT, AND THEN LET HIM ESCAPE. THEY TOOK THE VILLAGE BOY TO PASS HIM OFF AS THE PRINCE TO THE FOREIGN KING AND COLLECT THEIR REWARD.

THE DRIVERS REMAIN SILENT WHEN THE SORRY TALE IS FINISHED.

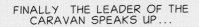

FINALLY THE LEADER OF THE CARAVAN SPEAKS UP...

WE ARE POOR MEN AND LEAD HARD LIVES. WE ARE ALSO AS WILLING AS ANYONE ELSE TO MAKE A FEW RUPEES EXTRA WHENEVER WE CAN.

BUT TO SELL AN INNOCENT BOY INTO CERTAIN DEATH...

WE'LL HAVE NO PART IN SUCH A DEED!

WE WILL TAKE THE BOY WITH US AND RETURN HIM TO HIS VILLAGE WHEN WE COME BACK. YOU TWO WILL BE LEFT HERE, BOUND. PERHAPS THE GODS WILL HAVE MERCY ON YOU. WE HAVE NONE!

LEAVING THE TWO MEN, THE CARAVAN CONTINUES ITS JOURNEY, TAKING THE BOY ALONG.

THEN I'M NOT TO SAY I'M PRINCE BHARAT ANYMORE?

THAT'S RIGHT, AND FORGET ABOUT THE FINE CLOTHES TOO.

AT THE SAME TIME, TULLUS COMES TO A FORK ON THE MOUNTAIN TRAIL...

NOW WHICH TRAIL SHALL WE TAKE, BLAZE? THE LEFT ONE BEARS MORE TO THE NORTH, SO WE'LL TAKE THAT!

I CAN'T SEE ANY TRACKS, BLAZE. WE'LL JUST HAVE TO PRAY THEY WENT THIS WAY!

A FEW MILES AHEAD OF TULLUS, THE TWO MEN HE IS FOLLOWING ARE STRUGGLING TO GET FREE.

STOP BLAMING ME FOR THE FIX WE'RE IN. SPEND YOUR STRENGTH ON GETTING OUT OF THESE ROPES.

AFTER A HARD STRUGGLE THEY MANAGE TO THROW OFF THE ROPES...

THOSE CARAVAN DRIVERS FRIGHTENED YOU OUT OF YOUR WITS.

BAH! YOU PROVED TO BE THE COWARD I ALWAYS KNEW YOU WERE!

FINALLY THEIR WORDS TURN TO BLOWS... AND AFTER A VICIOUS STRUGGLE ONE RUNS OFF, LEAVING HIS COMPANION LYING UNCONSCIOUS ALONGSIDE THE ROAD.

SUDDENLY FROM AROUND A CORNER STAGGERS A SKELETON-THIN MAN WAVING TULLUS BACK...

THE RAGGED FIGURE DOESN'T UTTER A SOUND. STANDING IN THE MIDDLE OF THE STREET HE RAISES HIS STICK TO BAR TULLUS FROM COMING ANY CLOSER!

THEN, WITH GESTURES, HE INDICATES THAT ALL THE PEOPLE HAVE FLED INTO THE HILLS...THAT HE ALONE IS LEFT AND THAT TULLUS MUST NOT COME INTO THE VILLAGE.

SUDDENLY TULLUS REALIZES WHAT THE POOR, STARVING MAN IS TRYING TO TELL HIM...

CHOLERA! THE TERRIBLE PLAGUE HAS STRUCK THIS VILLAGE!

JUST THEN, THE MAN WHO HAS BEEN LYING ON BLAZE'S BACK, COMES TO AND SLIDES OFF BLAZE TO THE GROUND.

WATER! WATER! MY THROAT IS ON FIRE. GIVE ME WATER!

BUT ALL THE WATER IN THE CHOLERA-RAVAGED VILLAGE IS TOO POLLUTED TO DRINK! TULLUS HELPS THE WOUNDED MAN ONTO BLAZE AGAIN, AND LEADS HIS FAITHFUL HORSE INTO THE HILLS TO LOOK FOR CLEAN, PURE WATER.

NO SOONER DOES HE GET OUTSIDE THE VILLAGE THAN HE IS MET WITH A SHOWER OF ROCKS AND SHOUTS OF ANGER!

GO AWAY, GO AWAY! COME NO CLOSER!